TIMELESS TALES

Folktales

Retold by TANA REIFF

Illustrated by CHERI BLADHOLM

NEW READERS PRESS

ISBN 0-88336-271-6

Copyright © 1991
New Readers Press
Division of ProLiteracy Worldwide
1320 Jamesville Ave., Syracuse, New York 13210

Printed in the United States of America

Project editor: Elizabeth Costello
Manuscript editor: Mark Legler
Designer: Patricia Rapple
Illustrator: Cheri Bladholm
Cover designer: The WD Burdick Company
Sponsoring editor: Marianne Ralbovsky

9 8

Contents

Introduction

Perhaps people are just born with the need to tell and listen to stories. Long before there was TV, long before there were books, people told stories. As long as there have been people, there have been folktales.

Folktales are stories that people tell over and over through the years. Each time a new person tells the story, it's a little different. The story grows and changes. That is why you might hear two stories with some parts the same and other parts very different. Yet the main meaning of the story is the same in both tellings.

What makes a story a folktale? A folktale is not written by one person who sits down to write a story. Rather, a folktale belongs to everyone. It begins with one person telling the story out loud. Over the years, other people tell the same story. Then one day someone might write the story down.

But many folktales have never been written down. Do you know a story that your parents or grandparents told you that you have never read anywhere? Such a story is probably a folktale. Of course, even after a folktale has been printed, people may still tell the story out loud.

For this book, we chose some famous folktales from around the world. You may already know some of these stories. Or they may sound like some stories you know. "The Shoes of Jewels" is from Vietnam, but it sounds very much like the French fairy tale, "Cinderella."

Some of these folktales teach a lesson. Some try to explain life or nature. Some are just good stories. All of them are fun to read.

The Man in the Moon

China

 Once there were two neighbors. They were very different from each other. The one man was kind to everyone. The other wanted everything for himself. Still, they were friends.

One day the two were walking together by the river. There on the path lay a little bird with a broken wing. The kind man said, "I want to take this bird home. I can fix its wing. I can care for it until it can fly again."

"What's the point?" asked the neighbor. "You can't fix that wing. It will never heal. This bird will only bring you trouble."

But the kind man took the bird home anyway. The wing healed. When the time came, the man carried the bird outside to let it fly away.

Then an amazing thing happened. The bird began to talk! "You saved my life," it said to the kind man. "I want to thank you. Here is a very special cucumber seed. Put it in the ground. Water it. The seed will grow into a vine. Take care of the vine and you will get some wonderful cucumbers."

The man did as the bird said. In a few months he picked the first cucumber. When he cut it open, he found another surprise. Inside the cucumber were gold and silver coins. The man cut open another cucumber. Gold and silver poured out of that one, too. Believe it or not, all the cucumbers were filled with gold and silver. Thanks to that bird, the man was rich!

When the kind man's neighbor heard about the cucumbers, he wanted to be rich, too. He headed for the river path to look for another hurt bird. Birds flew all around him. But none had fallen down with a broken wing.

So the selfish neighbor found a stick shaped like a Y. He found a long blade of river grass and stretched it across the Y. He placed a stone inside. Then he shot the stone into the air and hit a bird. The bird fell to the ground with a broken wing.

"I will take you home," said the selfish man to the bird. "I will nurse you back to health. When you are well, I want a cucumber seed as thanks."

Sure enough, the bird's wing healed. The bird gave the man a cucumber seed and flew away.

Like his kind friend, this man planted the seed. Pretty soon, a vine began to grow. It grew and grew and grew. It grew higher than the trees, into the sky, and into the heavens.

"My gold and silver must be on the moon," the man told himself. "I must go up the vine."

So he began to climb the vine. He went up and up. He went above the trees, into the sky, and into the heavens.

Did he ever find his gold and silver? We don't know for sure. The man never returned. The vine dried up and fell back down. Next time you see a full moon, look hard at it. You'll see that man. He sits all alone, far away, on the cold, cold moon.

Lazy Jack

England

 Jack was a lazy boy who lived with his mother. The two of them were very poor. Why so poor? Because lazy Jack did nothing but sit around. He didn't make any money. He didn't even do his share of the housework.

"You go out and make some money," said Jack's mother. "Or I will stop feeding you!"

Well, this lit a fire under that lazy Jack. The next day, he went to work for a farmer. At the end of a long, hard day, the farmer gave Jack a penny.

On the way home, Jack lost the penny. When he got home, his mother was angry. "You should have put it in your pocket," she said.

"Next time, next time," said Jack.

The next day, Jack went to work for a cow keeper. At the end of a long, hard day, the cow keeper gave Jack a jar of milk. Jack remembered his mother's words. He put the jar in his pocket.

On the way home, the milk spilled in his pocket. When he got home, his mother was angry. "You should have carried it on your head," she said.

"Next time, next time," said Jack.

The next day, Jack went to work for another farmer. At the end of a long, hard day, the farmer gave Jack some cheese. Jack remembered his mother's words. He carried the cheese on his head.

On the way home, the cheese melted into his hair. When Jack got home, his mother was angry. "You should have carried it in your hands," she said.

"Next time, next time," said Jack.

The next day, Jack went to work for a baker. At the end of a long, hard day, the baker gave him a big cat. Jack remembered his mother's words. He carried the cat in his hands.

On the way home, the cat scratched him, so he let it go. When Jack got home, his mother was angry. "You should have tied a string to it and pulled it behind you," she said.

"Next time, next time," said Jack.

The next day, Jack went to work for a butcher. At the end of a long, hard day, the butcher gave him some meat. Jack remembered his mother's words. He tied a string to the meat and pulled it behind him.

On the way home, the meat got all dirty on the ground. When Jack got home, his mother was angry. "You should have carried it on your shoulder," she said.

"Next time, next time," said Jack.

The next day, Jack went to work for yet another farmer. At the end of a long, hard day, the farmer gave him a donkey. Jack remembered his mother's words. He carried the donkey on his shoulder.

On the way home, Jack passed the house of a rich man and his daughter. The daughter was very beautiful, but she never laughed. Her father had said that the first man to make her laugh could marry her.

Just as Jack walked by, the daughter looked
out the window. She spotted Jack, carrying
a big old donkey on his shoulder, and she
laughed. She couldn't stop! She laughed
and laughed.

You can guess the end of the story.
Jack and the rich man's daughter were
married. He and his mother moved in with
the rich folks. And Jack never had to work
another day in his life.

Money
or
Mind

India

 Long ago, a prince and a store-
keeper's son were friends. They
liked to do the same things. Their
only difference was that the prince
was rich and the storekeeper's
son was not.

"My family has lots and lots of money,"
the prince said. "I could buy anything in
the world!"

"Money cannot buy everything," the storekeeper's son said. "It takes a good mind to
get ahead in the world."

"You are wrong, my friend," said the prince.

"Let's find out who is right," said the storekeeper's son. "Let's go to another country where no one knows us. Let's find out who does better after one year."

"Let's go!" said the prince.

Off they went together to another country. Once there, the prince bought a big house. The storekeeper's son found a job as a teacher.

Everything was going fine for both young men. Then one day the prince ran out of money. He came to see his friend. "Help me," begged the prince. "I have lost my house. I am hungry. What am I going to do?"

"Find a job," said the storekeeper's son.

So the prince went to work on a farm. The work was hard and dirty. And the farmer was mean. "I will give you only enough rice to fit on a leaf," he told the prince. "You'll get no money until you show me you can work."

The first day, the prince took the cows out to the field. But he couldn't get them to come back in again.

Then the prince gave the cows some water. But the water tray had holes in it, and all the water was lost.

The farmer was not happy with the prince's work. So he gave him only a tiny leaf of rice. That night, the prince went to sleep hungry.

The next day, his friend came to visit. The storekeeper's son felt sorry for the hungry prince. "I will work on the farm for you," said the storekeeper's son. "You teach school."

So the two young men traded jobs. The prince was no better at teaching than he had been at farm work. The storekeeper's son made out much better on the farm than the prince had.

The storekeeper's son took the cows out to the field. He took along a rope and tied the cows to a tree. He had no problem bringing them back in.

Then the storekeeper's son gave the cows some water. He saw the holes in the water tray and plugged them shut.

That night, he brought the farmer a big leaf. The farmer saw he had done a good job and filled the leaf with rice.

Whatever the farmer asked, the store-keeper's son found a way to do it. Before long, the farmer had to pay him not only with rice but with money, too.

At the end of the year, the farmer was happy to see the young man go. The store-keeper's son was smart. He was costing the farmer too much money.

The two young men went back home together. "You were right, my friend," said the prince. "Now I know. Money cannot buy everything. It takes a good mind to get along in the world."

"Money doesn't last," added the store-keeper's son. "But your mind is something to keep and use your whole life."

The Shoes of Jewels

Vietnam

 Cam was a pretty, happy young woman. Her sister Tam was not pretty because she was not happy.

One day, their mother sent them out to catch some fish for dinner. "See who catches the most fish," said the mother. "I will give that sister a jade necklace."

Off Cam and Tam went with their nets. In short order, Cam had caught nine fish. Tam caught only one. Still, Tam wanted that necklace. So she played a trick on Cam.

"See that lovely lotus flower over there?" Tam asked. "Will you go pick it for Mother?"

Cam put down her net. When she got back, her bucket was empty. Tam had taken off with all the fish.

Just then, Cam heard a voice. "Someday you will marry a prince and live in a big house," said the voice. "Look in your bucket. You will see a little blue fish. Take care of this fish."

Cam looked in her bucket. Sure enough, there was one little blue fish. "I will take care of this fish," said Cam. "I promise."

Cam took the fish home. There she found Tam, wearing the jade necklace. But Cam was happy anyway. She had her little blue fish.

Then Tam asked Cam to go out and gather some wood. When Cam came back, her little blue fish was gone. Tam had killed it and put its bones under a big tree.

Cam was very, very sad.

Just then, Cam heard the voice again. "Go out to that big tree," it told her. "Dig a hole under the tree."

Cam dug the hole and found the bones of the little blue fish.

"Now take those bones," said the voice. "Put them under your bed. Then wait 100 days."

When 100 days had passed, Cam looked under her bed. The bones were gone. In their place was a beautiful pair of shoes. The shoes were covered with shiny jewels. Cam put them on her feet. They fit just right.

Cam wore the shoes every day. One day, she was working in the field. She left the shoes by the path as she worked. A big bird dipped down and took one of her beautiful shoes. Up, up, and away it flew. The bird dropped the shoe right into the king's garden.

The next morning the king's son, the prince, found the beautiful shoe. It so happened that the prince was looking for a wife. He knew at once that the woman whose foot fit into this shoe must be very special. She would be the right woman for him.

So the prince put up a big sign. It said:

I will marry the
woman whose foot
fits the
Shoe of Jewels

Hundreds of young women lined up. They all wanted to marry the prince. They all tried on the shoe of jewels. But the shoe fit none of them.

Then came Cam. She remembered what the voice had told her: "Someday you will marry a prince and live in a big house." She put her foot into the shoe. It fit just right.

Cam and the prince set a wedding date. This made Tam angry, so she cooked up another trick. "Let's go to the woods and pick flowers," said Tam.

In the woods, Tam hit Cam on the head. Cam fell down. She was out cold. Tam left her there and went home. Lucky for Cam, an old woman found her and took her in. Cam got well again, but she could remember nothing from her past. She even forgot the prince.

The prince, however, did not forget Cam. He looked everywhere for her. And he always carried the shoe of jewels in his pocket.

One day, the prince was out walking. He stopped at the old woman's house in the woods for a drink. And who should bring him a cup of tea but Cam!

The prince knew her at once. But Cam did not know him. Then the prince pulled the shoe of jewels from his pocket. "Try this on," he said.

Seeing the shoe made Cam remember everything. She put her foot in the shoe. It fit just right.

Cam and the prince were married the next day. It was the first day of their long, happy life together.

Introduction to
"Aladdin's Lamp"

 Once there was a sultan, or
king, who didn't trust women.
So he would marry a woman,
then kill her the same night.
That way, she could never do
him wrong. But one wife found
a way to stay alive, and to save all the other
women. Her name was Scheherazade (shuh-
HAIR-uh-ZAHD). Here is what she did.

Each night she would begin telling the
sultan a wonderful story. She made sure she
was at a high point in the story at the end of
the night. Right at that point, she would stop
talking. The sultan had to let her live another
day so that he could hear the end of the
story. The next night, Scheherazade would
again stop her story at a high point. She did
this night after night for a thousand and one
nights. Her long stories saved her life. Here is
one of the most famous.

Aladdin's Lamp

Middle East

 Aladdin was a boy who had a mother but no father. They were very poor. One day, a man came up to him in the street. "I am your father's brother," he said. Aladdin had never seen the man before.

"My father is dead," said Aladdin.

"Oh, I did not know," said the man. "Here is some money. I want to buy dinner for you and your mother."

So Aladdin took the man home. "I never knew my husband had a brother," said his mother. But she took the man's money and made a lovely dinner for the three of them.

Day by day, Aladdin found out more about the man, who seemed to have magic powers. In fact, he was a wizard, but Aladdin did not know this.

One afternoon, the wizard took Aladdin out to the country. He showed him a large stone. "Only you can lift this stone," said the wizard. "Under it, you will see some steps. Go down the steps. At the bottom, you will find some fruit trees. At the end of the line of fruit trees is a wall. In that wall, you will find an oil lamp. Pour out the oil and bring me the empty lamp."

Then the wizard took a ring off his finger. He gave it to Aladdin. "Wear this," he said. "It will keep you safe."

Aladdin did as the wizard said. Sure enough, he found the lamp. He carried it back up the steps.

But as he climbed, he heard the wizard's voice. "The lamp will be mine," the wizard said. "Now I can get rid of the boy."

"You are not my uncle!" Aladdin called. "I won't give you the lamp!"

The wizard was so angry that he pushed the stone back into place and ran off. Poor Aladdin was stuck under the stone.

Then Aladdin remembered the ring. He rubbed

it, and out came a genie. A genie is a magic person who can give people anything they wish. "What can I do for you?" the genie of the ring asked Aladdin.

"Get me back home," said the boy. Just like that, Aladdin, the ring, and the lamp were back home with Aladdin's mother. It was dinnertime. But there was nothing in the house to eat or drink.

For something to do, Aladdin's mother began to polish the old oil lamp. As she rubbed, another genie, the genie of the lamp, popped out. "What can I do for you?" the genie asked.

"Get us some food and drink," said the mother. Just like that, food and drink of all kinds appeared. A beautiful meal rested upon golden dishes.

"Now get rid of the lamp," his mother told Aladdin. "I don't like all this magic stuff. We'll sell the golden dishes and live on that money."

Aladdin sold the dishes. But he did not get rid of the lamp. Instead, he hid it under the floor. Whenever he and his mother needed money, he rubbed the lamp and asked the genie for more golden dishes.

Five years passed. Aladdin grew into a young man. One day, he saw the sultan's daughter for the first time. Aladdin knew right away that he wanted to marry this princess. So he pulled out the lamp and gave it a rub. "What can I do for you?" asked the genie.

"Give me some jewels," said Aladdin. Just like that, a pile of beautiful, shiny jewels was before him. "Take these to the sultan," he told his mother. "Tell him he may have the jewels if I may marry his daughter."

His mother did, and the sultan was very
pleased. "But first," said the sultan, "I need
something else. Your son must send me
40 golden dishes full of jewels, carried
by 40 strong men."

Aladdin rubbed the lamp. Just like that,
40 golden dishes full of jewels, carried
by 40 strong men, were on their way to the
sultan. Aladdin's mother walked at the head
of the line.

The sultan was very, very pleased. "Your
son may marry my daughter," he said. "The
wedding will be today."

Aladdin and the princess were married.
They asked the genie for a big, beautiful
house. There they lived in happiness.

But word of the grand wedding and big
house reached the wizard. He knew it was all
because of the genie. He knew the man of
the house must be Aladdin.

The wizard saw this as another chance to get the lamp. So one day he stood outside Aladdin's home. "New lamps for old!" he called.

Aladdin was not home. The princess did not know the lamp was magic. She ran outside, gave the wizard the old lamp, and brought in a new one.

Outside, the wizard rubbed the magic lamp. "What can I do for you?" asked the genie.

"Take me and Aladdin's beautiful house to Africa!" said the wizard.

When Aladdin came home, the house and princess were gone. The sultan was angry beyond words. "I will find your daughter," promised Aladdin.

Aladdin looked all over. He could find no house and no princess. Then he remembered the magic ring, still on his finger. He rubbed it, and out came the genie of the ring. "What can I do for you?" the genie asked.

"Bring back my princess and my house," said Aladdin.

"I do not have such power," said the genie. "I am the genie of the ring, not of the lamp."

"Can you take me to my wife?" Aladdin asked.

"Yes, I can do that," said the genie of the ring. Just like that, Aladdin was in Africa, in front of his house. The princess looked out and saw him there. "Come in!" she called, happy to see her husband.

"Where is the lamp?" Aladdin asked.

"Inside the wizard's robe," answered the princess.

"We must get it back," said Aladdin. He and the princess came up with a plan.

That night, the princess gave the wizard a drink with poison in it. The wizard fell fast asleep. They took the lamp from his robe and gave it a rub. "What can I do for you?" asked the genie of the lamp.

"Take us and our house back home," said Aladdin and the princess. Just like that, they and their house were back in their own country, safe and sound. The sultan was full of joy to have them back. Aladdin and the princess lived in peace from that day on. They never heard from the evil wizard again.

Making Rain

Kenya

 In some parts of the world, it doesn't rain for a long, long time. This is what happens on the plains of Africa. When there is no rain for a long, long time, there is trouble.

When there is no rain, the grass dries up. If there is no grass, the birds cannot build their nests. Where will they lay their eggs? If there is no grass, the cows have nothing to eat. How will they keep from going hungry?

When there is no rain, the leaves on the trees cannot grow. If there are no leaves, the wild animals have no shade. How will they stay cool? If there are no leaves, the giraffes have nothing to eat. How will they feed themselves?

In one part of Africa, there had been no rain for a long, long time. A large black cloud hung over the plain, like a big umbrella. It looked like a rain cloud. But the rain did not come. So there was no grass. And there were no leaves.

Looking for something green, the birds and cows and giraffes and other wild animals began to walk. They walked and walked across the plain. But they could not find a place with grass and leaves. They became very hungry and very hot.

The leader of the plains people was worried. He, too, walked across the plain. He saw the thin cows. He heard them moo for help. He did not know how to help them. He watched the black cloud above and hoped for rain.

Then a great thing happened. A huge bird flew over the man. A long, beautiful feather fell from the bird. It brushed the man on the head as it fell to earth.

"Can this be the help we need?" wondered the man. "What should I do with this feather?"

He began to think. He came up with an idea. He found a stick. He tied the feather to the stick to make an arrow. Then he made a bow from which he could shoot the arrow.

He placed the feathered arrow in the bow. He pulled back the string of the bow. He shot that arrow right into the black cloud above him.

And then another great thing happened. The arrow shot a hole in the cloud. Rain gushed from the cloud. Down fell the rain. The dry plain drank up the water. The cows let out a big moo. The birds began to sing.

The rain kept on falling for many days. Soon, there was grass. And there were leaves. The birds built nests again. The cows and giraffes got fat again. The wild animals had shade again. All the plain was green.

And now, if the rain does not come for a very long time, the leader of the plains people knows what to do. He makes an arrow out of a feather. He looks for a big, black cloud. And he shoots a hole in the cloud to let out the rain. Rain is important, the leader knows. He will do all he can to make rain.

The Happy Man's Shirt

Italy

 There once was a young man who had everything in the world. He had brains. He had money. He lived in a fine house. But he wasn't happy. He sat around all day feeling sad.

The young man's father worried about him. "What is the matter?" he asked his son. "How can I help you to be happy? Can I help you find a wife? Can I send you off to school?"

"No, no," said the young man. "There is nothing you can do. I am just not a happy person."

His father didn't want to hear such talk. He wanted his son to be happy. It was the only thing in life he wanted.

So the father came up with a plan. He hired three people. "Go out and search for a happy man," he told them. "Bring him to me. If he is really happy, I will ask him for his shirt. Then I will give him my son's shirt."

The first searcher brought the father a priest. "Are you a happy man?" the father asked the priest.

"Oh, yes," said the priest. "But I would like to be king."

Someone who only wants to be someone else? This was not a happy man. "Keep your shirt," said the father.

The second searcher brought the father a rich man. "Are you a happy man?" the father asked the rich man.

"Oh, yes," said the rich man. "But I worry all the time about the end of the world."

Someone who worries about the end of the world? This was not a happy man. "Keep your shirt," said the father.

The third searcher brought the father a singer. "Are you a happy man?" the father asked the singer.

"Oh, yes," said the singer. "I wouldn't change a thing in my life."

"You *are* a happy man!" said the father. "Will you please help my son? Will you give him your shirt?"

The singer didn't answer.

"Please!" begged the father. "My son needs your shirt! Please may he have it?"

He reached for the singer's jacket. He ripped it open. And do you know what he found? Nothing. The happy man was not even wearing a shirt.

The
Tar
Baby

Africa/Southern U.S.

 One time all the animals dug a well for water. Br'er* Fox and Br'er Monkey and Br'er Elephant and Br'er Bear and even Sister Cow—they all helped. All the animals except Br'er Rabbit, that is. He just stood there and watched the others digging.

At last the well was dug. "Br'er Rabbit, you stay away from our well!" the animals told him. "Anyone who won't dig can't have any water."

---

* *Br'er* is a short form of *brother.*

The animals took turns watching the well. If Br'er Rabbit came near, they would chase him away.

But Br'er Rabbit was sly. He'd start singing a song. The animal who was watching the well would start dancing. And Br'er Rabbit would steal a drink.

Then came Br'er Fox's turn to watch the well. "I'll fix that guy," he said.

So Br'er Fox took some tar. He formed that tar into the shape of a baby. He put a big hat on that baby. And he sat that tar baby right beside the well.

Along came Br'er Rabbit. He saw the tar baby beside the well. "How do you do?" he asked it.

The tar baby didn't answer.

"Nice day, don't you say?" asked Br'er Rabbit.

The tar baby said nothing.

"Why don't you speak?" asked Br'er Rabbit. "Didn't your mama teach you manners?"

Still, the tar baby said nothing.

Br'er Rabbit was getting angry. He made a fist. He hit that tar baby smack in the face. But Br'er Rabbit's fist just stuck right on the tar baby's face. It wouldn't come off!

"Let me go!" shouted Br'er Rabbit.

But the fist stayed stuck.

Br'er Rabbit got so mad, he made another fist. He hit the tar baby on the other side of its face. And wouldn't you know it? Br'er Rabbit's other fist got stuck, too.

Just then, Br'er Rabbit heard someone laughing. Out came Br'er Fox from behind the trees. He was laughing to see Br'er Rabbit stuck to the tar baby.

"I got you!" Br'er Fox crowed. "You won't steal water from our well again, will you?" Then Br'er Fox took a long, cool drink for himself. "Hmmm," he said, right in Br'er Rabbit's face. "That is some mighty good water."

With that, Br'er Fox started building a wood pile. "I'm going to build a big fire and throw you on it," he said to Br'er Rabbit.

"What a good idea!" said Br'er Rabbit. "I'm glad you're going to throw me on your fire. I sure don't want you to throw me in that thorny briar patch."

"I sure don't want you to have your way," said Br'er Fox. "I'll throw you in the river instead of the fire."

"Well, thank goodness!" said Br'er Rabbit. "You know I can't swim. But I'd rather go in the river than in the briar patch!"

"All right, then," said Br'er Fox. "I'll throw you in the briar patch. We'll just see how you like it."

Br'er Fox picked up Br'er Rabbit. He swung the little guy around in a big circle about five times. Then he let go. "I got you this time!" Br'er Fox called after the flying bunny. Br'er Rabbit flew through the air and landed in the briar patch.

Br'er Fox waited to hear Br'er Rabbit yell out in pain. But he heard nothing. Then he heard "Ha! Ha!" coming from the briar patch.

"Fooled you!" called Br'er Rabbit. "The briar patch is my home. It doesn't scare me!" And away he skipped, still in one piece and laughing all the way.

Stone Soup

*France, Sweden,
and other places*

 There was a young man who
didn't have a home. People
called him a hobo. He went
from town to town on foot. In
each town, he would look for
something to eat and a place
to sleep.

In one town, he knocked on a door. An old
woman answered. "May I have a place to
sleep?" asked the hobo.

"I don't know you," said the old woman.
"Go away."

"We are all in this life together," said the hobo. "Surely you can help a person in need."

"Very well," said the old woman. "You may sleep on the floor."

"May I have something to eat?" the hobo then asked.

"I have nothing in the house to eat," said the old woman.

"Well, then, I will share what I have," said the hobo. "Do you have a large pot for making soup?"

The old woman got out a pot. The hobo filled the pot with water and put it on the stove. Then he pulled from his pocket a stone. He dropped that stone into the hot water.

"What in the world are you making?" the old woman asked.

"I am making stone soup," said the hobo as he stirred the pot. "This works quite well. However, my soup would taste much better if only it had some flour in it."

"Let me look around," said the old woman. "I may have a cup of flour somewhere." Sure enough, she did. The hobo put the flour into the pot and stirred.

"The soup is getting better," said the hobo. "However, it would taste much better if only it had some meat and potatoes in it."

"I'll go ask my neighbor," said the old woman. In a few minutes, she returned with some meat, potatoes, and a neighbor man.

 "What is this soup you are making?" asked the neighbor man.

"It is stone soup," said the hobo. "It's getting better by the minute. However, it would taste ever so much better with a carrot in it."

"I'll get you a carrot," said the neighbor man. In a few minutes, he returned with a carrot and a neighbor woman.

"This soup is getting very thick and delicious," said the hobo. "However, a few more vegetables would really make it taste wonderful."

The neighbor woman went to look for vegetables. In a few minutes, she returned with a whole bunch of vegetables and a whole bunch of neighbors. Each neighbor added something to the soup—more potatoes, a cup of milk, some corn, beans, and many other things.

At last it was time to eat the soup. "Won't you all join in the feast?" said the hobo. "We all made the soup together and we shall all enjoy it!"

"Well, I do say!" cried the old woman. "This is the best soup I have ever tasted. I never knew anyone could make such fine soup from just a stone and some water!"

All the neighbors enjoyed the stone soup and each other's company. The hobo had a good night's sleep. And the next day he set out on the road once again.